ISBN: 002-688518-2

A Ready, Set, · Read! Book

# Randy Raccoon
## and the
# Big Mess

**Written by Helene Chirinian**
**Illustrated by Mary Ann Fraser**

**CHEX BOOKS · NEW YORK**

It was a lovely Saturday morning. The Raccoon family was eating breakfast. "Grandma and Grandpa Raccoon asked us to visit them today," said Randy's mother. "Try to keep clean, Randy. It's not nice to visit people when you look messy. So, please comb your hair and wash off your milk mustache." But just then, Randy spilled the milk.

"Oops!" he said. "I'll help clean up."

His mother said, "I'll do it, Randy. It's okay."

"Please find something to do until we leave, Randy," said his father. "Something that isn't messy, spilly, or sticky."

"I'm going to paint pictures. Aunt Ruth gave me a new paint set." And Randy went away to his room.

Randy took out his paints and some paper. He opened the paints, one by one. "I'll paint a picture of me," he said to himself. Randy painted with green, blue, brown, and red. "It looks just like me," he smiled.

He didn't notice that his elbow was in the paint.

Randy painted and painted. He liked his picture a
lot. Before he knew it, Mom was calling him.

"Randy, it's time to leave for Grandma and Grandpa's
house. Put everything away and come down." Randy
tried to put everything away fast.

Randy's father came upstairs. "I just thought I'd give you a hand," he said to Randy. Then he saw paints all over the floor and all over Randy.

"Oh, no! What a mess! What happened, Randy?"

Randy said, "I don't know, Daddy. I started out neat and ended up messy."

"Well, we can't leave the room like this. And look at you! You have paint all over yourself! You can't visit Grandma and Grandpa looking like this!"

Randy wiped his face with his sleeve. But he only made it worse because his sleeves had been dipped in the paint.

"I think you'd better take a bath, young man," said Randy's father. "Come down when you're nice and clean." And he left Randy's room.

Randy ran the bath water. "I forgot to get clean
clothes," he said to himself. Randy went back into his
room and picked out blue overalls. Then he chose a
green shirt and some purple socks.

"Now I'll take my bath," Randy said. But when he
got to the bathroom, the tub was full and water was
running over the sides. The floor was flooded. "Oh, no,
how did this tub fill up so fast!" he cried. Randy shut
off the water, took a towel, and started to wipe up
water from the floor.

Just then Mrs. Raccoon came in. "What happened here? What a mess!"

"I didn't mean to make a mess," Randy said. "First, I painted a nice picture. Stuff spilled. I was full of paint, so I had to take a bath. Then..."

Mrs. Raccoon just shook her head. "No more excuses, please. Let's clean up this mess and get you ready."

The Raccoons got in their car and went to visit
Grandma and Grandpa. Grandma and Grandpa had a
big hug ready for Randy.

Grandpa said, "I bet I know what you'd like."

"Chocolate-peppermint cookies!" said Randy. And he
ran into the kitchen.

Suddenly, there was a big crash in the kitchen.
Randy was sitting in the middle of the floor. Pieces of
the cookie jar were all around him. So were cookies.
"What happened?" asked Grandpa. "Are you okay?"

Randy stood up and brushed himself off. "I'm okay,
Grandpa. I tried to get cookies. The jar fell. But I got
one cookie, see?" He also had chocolate all over his
face and on Grandma's nice tablecloth, too.

Randy's father looked very angry. "Randy, you make
a lot of messes. But now you've made one in
Grandma's house!"

But Grandma hugged Randy and said, "Never mind.
Boys will be boys, and little raccoons just get into
everything."

"Why don't you go outside and play in the garden?" asked Grandpa kindly. "You can keep out of trouble there." He led Randy out of the house.

"Look at the beautiful flowers," Randy said. He walked around the garden.

"Oh! There are weeds here, too. I'll help Grandpa. I'll get some tools and pull them out."

17

Randy saw the tools across the garden. But, there was a big mud puddle in the way. "I can jump right across it." Randy jumped as far as he could. Then, splat! He landed right in the puddle.

Randy waded out of the puddle and got the tools. "I guess I got a little messy again," he said to himself. He pulled lots of weeds from the garden.

Then Randy picked some flowers and ran into the house.

Randy's mother and father shouted, "Oh, no!"

Grandpa said, "That boy is a mess."

And Grandma sighed, "You need a bath." She led him into the bathroom and popped him right into the tub.

When they got home from Grandma and Grandpa's, Randy's mother and father said, "Randy, you get jam on the walls. You sat on your tuna sandwich last week. How can you stop making messes?"

Randy could not think of a thing. He went to bed, still thinking. Then he sat up and said out loud, "I just won't do anything. Then I won't make messes."

"I won't make one mess in school today," Randy said as he walked into class on Monday.

"Let's get started. Randy, you may play with clay today," said Mrs. Otter.

Randy answered, "If I play with clay, I'll get it all over everybody and everyplace. I don't want to make a mess today."

"Let's play in the sand, Randy!" said Bonnie Bunny
and Bobby Beaver after lunch.

"No, thank you," said Randy, "I don't want to make
a mess." So he sat alone on the bench. He stayed nice
and clean. But he wasn't very happy.

"Do you want to come to my house?" asked Bobby
Beaver after school."

"No, thank you," said Randy sadly, "I don't want to
make a mess. I might spill something. I make a mess
every place." And Randy walked home slowly by
himself.

"Did you have a good day at school today?" asked Mr. and Mrs. Raccoon when Randy got home.

"No," answered Randy, "but I didn't make one mess." Randy did look very clean and neat.

"Why don't you paint a picture? We like your pictures," smiled Randy's father.

Randy shook his head. "No, painting makes a big mess."

"What can we do to help Randy?" Randy's mother asked Mr. Raccoon.

"He doesn't want to be messy. But he isn't having any fun," said Randy's father. "If Randy would just be more careful, he could still have fun." The Raccoons thought. Then Mr. Raccoon said, "I have an idea!" He ran into the living room and called two of Randy's friends.

Randy was in his room thinking of something to do. "I could read, but I might tear pages. I could play trucks, but they might run into the wall. I could color, but I might squish crayons on the floor. I can't do anything. Being neat is very hard work." Then Randy heard the doorbell ring. "I'll get it," he said. He answered the door. There were two of his friends!

"What are you guys doing here?" he asked.

Bonnie Bunny said, "We were invited. Let's play!"

"Wait!" said Randy. "We'll make a mess." Just then his mother came to the door.

"Don't worry, Randy. You can have fun if you're careful. We'll cover the floor so paint doesn't get on it. You can all wash your hands when you're finished painting."

Randy asked Bonnie and Bobbie Beaver to come in.

"I can be careful," Randy said. "I'll start right now." And he did.

# Ready Set Read! Words To Learn

**Note to parent:**

*The word list from the story you have just read and the activity that follows will teach your child reading and comprehension skills. Read the words to your child, then encourage him or her to read them. The list will give your child a good beginning reading vocabulary.*

| | | | | | | | |
|---|---|---|---|---|---|---|---|
| visit | keep | messy | wash | try | all | the | b |
| look | milk | spilled | sticky | took | picture | green | b |
| brown | red | everything | fast | don't | know | bath | n |
| down | come | cookie | meet | house | garden | tools | f |
| school | think | father | much | table | today | new | p |

Look at each picture.
With your finger, point to the
word that spells the name
of each.

**paint**

**garden**

**jam**

**tub**

**bench**

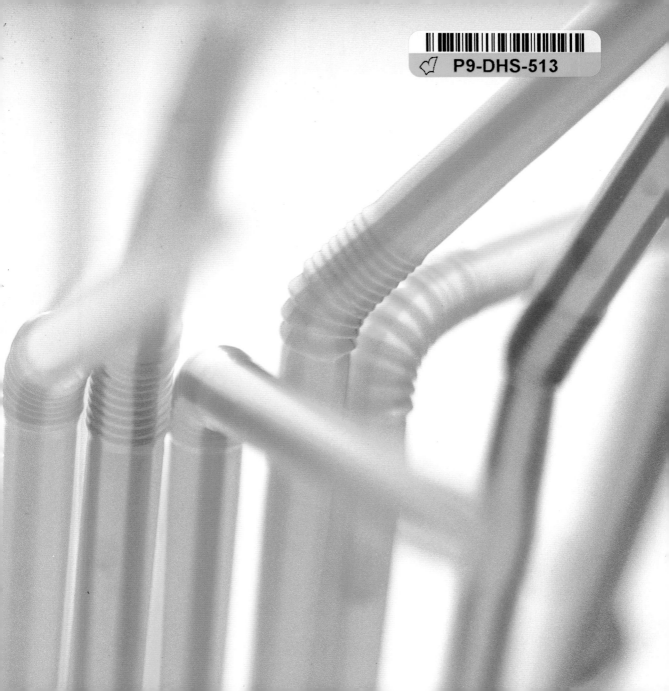

SMOOTHIES AND SHAKES

Elsa Petersen-Schepelern

*photography by* **Debi Treloar**

# SMOOTHIES AND SHAKES

RYLAND
PETERS
& SMALL

LONDON NEW YORK

| | |
|---|---|
| **Senior Designer** | Ashley Western |
| **Editor** | Maddalena Bastianelli |
| **Production** | Patricia Harrington |
| **Art Director** | Gabriella Le Grazie |
| **Publishing Director** | Alison Starling |
| **Food Stylist** | Elsa Petersen-Schepelern |
| **Stylist** | Helen Trent |

**Author's Acknowledgements:**
My thanks to my sister Kirsten, my nephews Peter Bray and Luc Votan, and Luis
Peral-Aranda in Madrid. In India, thanks to Prem Anand, Executive Chef of the
Park-Sheraton Hotel in Madras (Chennai) and Shona Adhikari of the Welcomgroup.
Particular thanks go to Debi Treloar for her wonderful photographs and to her sons
Woody and Quinn who, as always, enthusiastically road-tested the recipes in this
book. Thanks also to stylist Helen Trent for her usual beautiful work.

Thanks also to the Conran Shop in Fulham Road, and Purves & Purves in
Tottenham Court Road, London, for lending us their gorgeous props.

**Notes:**
All spoon measurements are level unless otherwise stated.
Drinks in this book were made using a Waring Blender. Not all blenders are
designed for crushing ice: if yours isn't, put crushed or uncrushed ice cubes in
the glass, then pour the blended drink over them.

First published in the United States in 2001
by Ryland Peters & Small Inc.,
519 Broadway, 5th Floor
New York, NY 10012
10 9 8 7 6 5
www.rylandpeters.com

Text © Elsa Petersen-Schepelern 2001
Design and photographs © Ryland Peters & Small 2001

Printed and bound in China

ISBN 1 84172 165 4

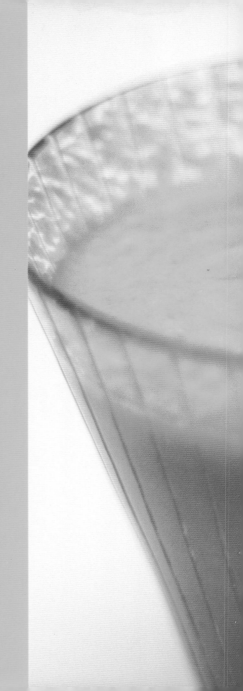

# contents

# good health in a glass...

One of the best things about smoothies is that they're so very good for you—but they taste so good they seem positively sinful. Fresh fruit and fruit juice provide many of the vitamins and minerals our bodies need. Doctors recommend we have at least five servings of fruit and vegetables a day—what better way to start the countdown. Add other good things, like yogurt, nut milks, and soy milk, and these drinks become vitamin powerhouses. Some recipes aren't so virtuous—chocolate and ice cream may not be exactly saintly—but they taste marvelous.

To make these delicious drinks, all you need is a blender—and very often not even that. I like to start with ice cubes blended to a snow. However, not all blenders are designed to crush ice, so if yours isn't, put the whole cubes in the serving glass, blend the rest of the ingredients, and pour them over the ice. Different brands of blender have different capacities. Most will make at least a one-serving smoothie, but to serve more people you may have to work in batches.

Many of the recipes have been written for one person—admittedly someone like myself with a large appetite—and can be made quickly and served for breakfast, for instance. Others can be made in bulk and served in big pitchers for a party or brunch. After standing for a few minutes, the ingredients will separate into layers. Don't be alarmed—although the goodness is best just after blending, the smoothies will still taste just as good.

# strawberry smoothie
## with **lime juice** and **mint**

A marvelous way to be absolutely self-indulgent. One small basket of strawberries should last you two days—or one day if you're being generous and making a smoothie for someone else. The rule with strawberries is to wash them just before hulling (removing the green frill and stalk)—otherwise they fill with water and you get a more watery strawberry.

**about 6 large ripe strawberries**
**4–6 ice cubes**
**juice of 1 lime**
**6 mint leaves, plus 1 sprig to serve**
**honey or sugar, to taste (optional)**

SERVES **1**

Put the ice cubes in a blender and work to a snow. Add the strawberries and blend until smooth.

Add the lime juice, mint, and sugar or honey, if using. Blend again and serve, topped with a sprig of mint.

**fruit smoothies**

Make your version of this tropical smoothie, depending on what's good in the market that day. Starfruit, lychees, melons of all sorts—all are good. Take care with colors though: red and green make gray—not appetizing in the color department.

# tropical fruit smoothie
## with **pineapple, watermelon, strawberries,** and **lime**

**2 limes**
**10 ice cubes**
**6 strawberries**
**1 small pineapple, peeled, cored, and chopped**
**3 thick slices watermelon, the flesh cut into**
   **wedges and seeded**
**your choice of other fruit such as:**
   **6 canned lychees, drained and seeded**
   **2 bananas, sliced**
   **1 cherimoya, seeded**
   **berries**
**sugar, to taste (optional)**

SERVES **4-6**

Finely slice one of the limes and reserve. Grate the zest and squeeze the juice of the other.

Put the ice cubes in a blender and work to a snow. Add all the prepared fruit, in batches if necessary, and blend until smooth. Add the lime zest and juice and blend again. Add sugar, if using, then serve in chilled glasses with slices of lime.

# pineapple ginger smoothie

A delicious fruit smoothie based on the sharbat—the beautiful sweetened fruit drink created for the imperial courts of Muslim rulers from Persia to Moorish Spain, from the Holy Land to Moghul India. Because Muslims don't drink alcohol and many of their lands are deserts, they have created an amazing array of non-alcoholic thirst-quenching drinks. This is, of course, the origin of our word "sherbet."

**1 inch fresh ginger, peeled and grated**
**1 medium pineapple, peeled, cored,**
**and chopped**
**sugar syrup or sugar, to taste**
**ice cubes, to taste**

SERVES **4**

Working in batches if necessary, put the ginger in a blender, add the pineapple and blend to a smooth purée, adding enough ice water to make the blades run. Taste and add sugar or sugar syrup to taste. Half-fill a pitcher with ice cubes, pour over the pineapple mixture, stir, and serve.

Alternatively, add about 10 ice cubes when blending.

Bananas make very good smoothies—add them to almost anything else and they will reward you with a sweet creaminess. Bananas have a special affinity with nuts, so peanut butter is gorgeous.

# banana and peanut butter smoothie

Cut the bananas into chunks. Put them into a blender with the remaining ingredients. Work to a purée. Thin with a little more milk or water if too thick, then serve.

**2 large, ripe bananas**
**10 ice cubes**
**1 tablespoon sugar or sugar syrup, or to taste**
**½ cup milk, yogurt, or half-and-half**
**¼ cup peanut butter**

SERVES **1**

Dried fruit smoothies make life easy when there isn't a single piece of fresh fruit left in the bowl. Just pop the dried fruit in a glass, cover with water, and leave in the refrigerator overnight. Next morning you have your delicious high-fiber fruit hit all ready for the blender.

# dried pear
## and **mint froth**

**6 dried pears**
**6 sprigs of mint**
**6 ice cubes**

SERVES **1**

Put the pears in a glass, cover with water, and chill for 4 hours or overnight. When ready to serve, put in a blender with the leaves from the mint. Add the soaking water and blend to a froth. If preferred, blend ice cubes with the other ingredients to make an icy froth, adding extra water if too thick. A terrific cooler for a sunny summer morning.

# breakfast shake
## with **dried apricots**

**6–8 dried apricots**
**6 ice cubes**
**honey, to taste**
**(optional)**

SERVES **1**

Put the apricots in a glass and cover with cold water. Chill for about 4 hours or overnight. When ready to use, discard the seeds if any, then transfer the flesh and soaking water to a blender. Add the ice cubes and blend to a thick shake. Taste and add a little honey if preferred.

# strawberry slush
## with **mango** and **lime**

This is a very good way of making one mango go just a little further. You can also freeze the mixture into delicious frozen treats to have later in the day (see the recipe on page 26).

**1 ripe mango, peeled, seeded, and chopped, or 1 cup**
**frozen or canned mango pieces**
**grated zest and juice of 1 lime**
**6 large strawberries, hulled and halved**
**6 ice cubes**
**sparkling water**
**honey or sugar, to taste (optional)**

SERVES **1–2**

Put the mango into a blender. Add the grated lime zest and juice and the strawberries. Add the ice cubes and blend to a froth. Add enough sparkling water to make the blades run and make the mixture to the consistency you prefer. Add honey or sugar, if using, then serve.

# rose petal apple cocktail

I tasted this gorgeous, refreshing drink in Madras, India, prepared by my friend, leading chef Prem Anand. If you live near an Asian or Caribbean market, you can buy cartons of sugarcane juice and coconut water (the liquid from inside the coconut, not coconut milk). If difficult to find, use all apple juice instead.

Chill all the ingredients except the rosebud. Put the coconut water and sugarcane juice—or apple juice—in a pitcher. Add the rosewater and honey to taste. Stir well and serve, sprinkled with rosepetals.

If preferred, you can add a little grated fresh coconut, and serve the drink in glasses half-filled with ice. This makes an impressive cocktail for non-drinkers.

**1 cup coconut water or apple juice**
**½ cup sugarcane juice or apple juice**
**1 teaspoon honey (optional)**
**a dash of rose water**
**petals from 1 rose bud**
**freshly grated coconut (optional)**

SERVES **2**

# thai papaya smoothie
## with **mint, lime,** and **condensed milk**

In Southeast Asia, street vendors sell plastic bags filled with drinks—often luridly colored. They are sealed and a straw provided to pierce the bag. Condensed milk is a common ingredient, used to add sweetness and creaminess. Use heavy cream if you prefer.

**10 ice cubes**
**1 papaya, peeled, halved, and seeded**
**juice of 1 lime**
**3 tablespoons sweetened condensed milk**
**6 mint leaves**

SERVES **2**

Put the ice cubes in the blender and work to a snow. Chop the papaya flesh and add to the blender. Add the lime juice, condensed milk, and mint leaves, blend again, then serve.

# summer fruit crush
## with **peach, nectarine, apricots,** and **raspberries**

Make this fruity mixture in bigger quantities for a party. I like it made with sparkling water, but you could use cherryade for a children's party. If the fruit is sweet and ripe you may not need sugar or honey.

**1 ripe peach, peeled and halved**
**1 ripe nectarine, halved**
**2 ripe apricots, halved**
**a handful of raspberries**
**6 ice cubes**
**sparkling water, to taste**
**honey or sugar (optional)**

SERVES **2**

Discard the pits from the fruit. Put all the fruit in a blender, add the ice and enough sparkling water to make the blades run. Blend to a purée.

Taste and add honey or sugar, if preferred, and enough extra water to produce the consistency you like. Pour into glasses and serve.

# frozen treats
## with **mango, berry,** and **passionfruit**

I discovered these treats when I was making a mango and strawberry smoothie one day and had just a little left over. A happy accident. Partially freeze them between each addition to keep the layers separate.

Put the strawberries in a blender, add the mango purée, and blend until smooth, adding water if necessary to make the consistency of thin cream.

Scoop the passionfruit flesh and seeds into a bowl and break up with a fork. Add sugar to taste, and stir until dissolved.

Spoon a layer of mango and strawberry mixture into each frozen treat mold, filling them about one-third full. Partially freeze.

Remove from the freezer and add a layer of passionfruit. Partially freeze. Do not freeze solid or it will be difficult to insert the sticks.

Remove from the freezer and add a final layer of mango and strawberry mixture. Insert the sticks, then freeze until hard.

**12 large, ripe strawberries, hulled and halved**
**2 cups canned mango purée or frozen mango**
**pieces, thawed and blended to a purée**
**4 ripe and wrinkled passionfruit**
**sugar, to taste**

plastic frozen treat molds, with sticks

MAKES **8**

**frozen smoothies**

# frozen watermelon, ginger, and lime

Watermelon makes a delicious drink and it is terrific with hot, spicy partners like chile and ginger—I use the lime zest and juice to point up the flavor. I find I don't need any extra sugar.

**1 ripe, round watermelon, about 18 inches
    diameter, halved and seeded**
**2 inches fresh ginger, peeled and grated**
**freshly squeezed juice of 2 limes**
**sugar, to taste (optional)**
**ice cubes, to serve**

SERVES **4**

Put the flesh of ½ the watermelon in a blender, add the ginger and lime juice, and blend until smooth, adding water if necessary. Taste, stir in sugar if using, pour into ice cube trays, and freeze. When ready to serve, put the remaining watermelon in the blender and blend until smooth. Put the ice cubes in 4 glasses, top with watermelon juice and serve.

# indian fresh frozen lime

In India, a typical summertime drink is the juice of a fresh lime, topped up with seltzer. I like to freeze the lime juice first.

**freshly squeezed juice of 6 large limes and
    shredded zest of 1 lime (optional)**
**sugar, to taste**
**sparkling water or seltzer**

SERVES **4**

Mix the lime juice with an equal amount of water and stir in sugar to taste. Pour into ice cube trays and freeze.

To serve, put the ice cubes into 4 glasses and top with sparkling water or seltzer. Add the lime zest if preferred.

# iced rose petal tea

**6 heaped teaspoons rose petal leaf tea**
**sugar or honey, to taste**
**1 teaspoon rose water**

TO SERVE:
**ice cubes**
**sparkling water**
**rose petals (optional)**

SERVES **8**

Put the tea and sugar or honey in a 4-cup French coffee press and cover with boiling water. Let steep for 1 minute, then strain into a pitcher. Let cool, then stir in the rose water. Chill.

Fill a pitcher with ice cubes and pour in half the tea. Add sparkling water and the remaining tea. Stir, top with rose petals, if using, then serve.

# iced orange flower tea

**6 heaped teaspoons orange pekoe leaf tea**
**sugar or honey, to taste**
**1 teaspoon orange flower water**

TO SERVE:
**ice cubes**
**sparkling water**
**shredded zest of 1 orange**

SERVES **8**

Put the tea and sugar or honey in a 4-cup French coffee press and cover with boiling water. Let steep for 1 minute, then strain into a pitcher. Let cool, then stir in the orange flower water. Chill.

Fill a pitcher with ice cubes and pour in half the tea. Add sparkling water and the remaining tea. Stir, top with orange zest, then serve.

# frozen grapes in pineapple juice

Frozen grapes are utterly delicious—the flesh turns to a sweet and scented snow. I think plain pineapple juice is sweet enough, but you may like to add sugar or honey to taste.

**about 24 large, sweet, seedless grapes**
**2 cups pineapple juice**

SERVES **4**

Arrange the grapes on a freezer tray and freeze.

When frozen, put into 4 chilled glasses, top with pineapple juice, then serve.

# fruit juice ice cubes with low-fat yogurt

The great advantage of fruit juice cubes is that they thaw very slowly. Children love them. Top up the glasses with yogurt or buttermilk.

**2 cups freshly squeezed fruit juice**
**    or fresh fruit purée, sweetened**
**    with sugar**
**2 cups low-fat yogurt**

SERVES **4**

Freeze the sweetened fruit juice or purée in ice cube trays.

When ready to serve, put the yogurt in a blender with ½ cup cold water. Blend to a froth. Fill 4 glasses with fruit cubes, then spoon in the yogurt and serve.

# frozen fruit juice granitas

Choose your favorite juices to make these granitas.
You might prefer one variety, or several. I find that thick
juices like pear, peach, and apricot are especially good.
Serve the ices straight after crushing—they melt fast.

**6 cups fruit juice or purée of your
choice, such as mango, cranberry,
pear, or organic apple juice**
**sugar, to taste**

SERVES **4-6**

Add sugar so that the juice is just a little sweeter than you
like to drink it (freezing reduces sweetness). Fill ice cube
trays with the fruit juice. Freeze.

When ready to serve, turn out into 4 small bowls and crush
with a fork—you are aiming for an icy texture, not smooth
like an ice cream. Serve in small glasses with spoons.
Alternatively, fill each glass with frozen juice cubes and top
with icy buttermilk.

# ice cream smoothies

## apricot ice cream smoothie
### with **cream**

Essence of apricots! These fruit, like peaches and nectarines, are too dense to squeeze for juice—you have to purée them in a blender. The ice cream makes the mixture even more indulgent. I always leave the peel on—it chops up into little pieces and gives a pretty color and an interesting texture. However, if you're using peaches, peel them first.

**3 ice cubes**
**2–3 ripe apricots, halved, seeded, and sliced**
**2 scoops vanilla or strawberry ice cream**
**about 1 cup apricot nectar**
**milk or water**
**2 tablespoons cream or yogurt, to serve**
   **(optional)**

SERVES **1**

Put the ice cubes in a blender and blend to a snow. Add the apricot slices, ice cream, and apricot nectar. Blend until frothing and creamy, adding enough milk or water to make the blades run.

Put the mixture into a glass, swirl in the cream or yogurt, if using, and serve with a spoon.

Cherries and chocolate are a marriage made in heaven.
When cherries are in season, pit them and stuff the cavity with
a candy-coated plain chocolate candies (I use M&Ms®.) Freeze
and use straight away with chocolate ice cream and a smoothie
made of pitted cherries—or keep them for later in the year,
when you need to remind yourself of the taste of summer.

# cherry-chocolate smoothie
## with **frozen cherries** stuffed with **M&Ms**®

**12** M&Ms®
**36 cherries, pitted**
**1 pint chocolate ice cream**
**12 ice cubes**
**ice water or milk (optional)**

SERVES **4**

Press M&Ms® into the cavities of 12 of the cherries.
Arrange apart on a tray and freeze.

When ready to serve, put the remaining pitted cherries
in a blender, add the ice cubes, and work to a purée,
adding a little ice water or milk, if necessary, to help
the machine run.

Put 3 scoops of chocolate ice cream in each of
4 tall glasses and pour over the puréed cherries.
Add some frozen cherries, then serve.

# strawberry ice cream smoothie

Strawberry smoothies are invariably the most popular with guests. Serve them made just with ice, or with yogurt, ice cream, or milk. Or (as here) with the lot: self-indulgence is a very good thing in my view.

**12 ice cubes**
**4 scoops strawberry ice cream**
**12 large ripe strawberries, hulled and halved**
**½ cup low-fat yogurt**
**low-fat milk**

SERVES **4**

Put the ice cubes in a blender and blend to a snow. Add the ice cream, strawberries, and yogurt and blend again, adding enough milk to give a creamy consistency. Pour into glasses and serve.

# blueberry ice cream smoothie

I love the ashes-of-roses blue-pink color of puréed blueberries. Somehow, I always think of them as a great match for chocolate, especially chocolate ice cream (always providing of course that I don't eat them long before they even get to the blender!).

**1 cup blueberries, chilled**
**2 scoops ice cream, chocolate
   or vanilla**
**low-fat milk, chilled**

SERVES **1**

Reserve a few blueberries to serve, then put the remainder into a blender.

Add 1 scoop chocolate ice cream and ½ cup milk, or enough to make the blades run. Blend to a purée, then add extra milk to taste (the less you add, the thicker the smoothie will be).

Pour the mixture into a glass and top with the reserved blueberries.

# iced coffee

Some people prefer this frothy iced coffee made with instant coffee. Personally, I much prefer the real thing, frozen into ice cubes.

**1 cup strong black espresso coffee, cooled**
**½ cup ice-cold milk, or to taste**
**3 scoops vanilla ice cream**
**unsweetened cocoa powder or chocolate**
**   jimmies**

SERVES **1**

Freeze the coffee in ice cube trays. When ready to serve, put the cubes in a blender, add the milk, and blend to a froth.

Put 2 scoops of the ice cream into a glass, pour over the iced coffee, top with a second scoop of ice cream, and sprinkle with cocoa powder or chocolate jimmies.

# mocha frappé

Dark chocolate ice cream and grated bittersweet chocolate make a marvelous mocha. If you don't have any bittersweet chocolate, use cocoa powder instead—it's also good, though not quite as sumptuous.

**1 cup strong black espresso coffee, cooled**
**½ cup ice-cold milk, or to taste**
**1 tablespoon unsweetened cocoa powder or**
**   grated dark chocolate, plus extra to serve**
**3 scoops dark chocolate ice cream**

SERVES **1**

Freeze the coffee in ice cube trays. When ready to serve, put the cubes in a blender, add the milk and cocoa powder or grated chocolate, and blend to a froth.

Put 2 scoops chocolate ice cream into a glass, pour over the iced coffee, top with a second scoop of ice cream, and sprinkle with grated dark chocolate.

# leche merengada

Last summer in Madrid, a Spanish friend introduced me to this wonderful traditional drink, half way between a milkshake and an ice cream. I use a hand-held stick blender to beat it, but you could also mash it with a fork and beat with a whisk.

**4 cups milk**
**1½ cups sugar**
**1 curl of lemon zest, plus grated lemon zest to serve**
**1 cinnamon stick, broken**

TO SERVE:
**grated lemon zest**
**powdered cinnamon**
**cinnamon sticks (optional)**

SERVES **4**

Put the milk, sugar, and curl of lemon zest in a saucepan and bring to a boil, stirring. Boil for 2 minutes, then remove from the heat and let cool.

Strain into a freezer-proof container, cover, and freeze.

When ready to serve, remove from the freezer. Using a hand-held blender, beat the frozen milk mixture to a creamy froth. Serve, sprinkled with powdered cinnamon and grated lemon zest, with cinnamon sticks for stirring.

# yogurt and buttermilk

Yogurt, whether low-fat or full-cream, is one of nature's wonder foods. It is one of the best ways to add calcium to the diet—especially important for women.

## raspberry yogurt smoothie

**4 cups raspberries**
**6–8 ice cubes**
**1 cup yogurt**
**sparkling water, low-fat milk, or buttermilk**
**mild honey or sugar, to taste (optional)**

SERVES **4**

Put the raspberries in a blender with the ice cubes, yogurt, and enough sparkling water or milk to make the machine run. Blend to a thin froth, adding more sparkling water or milk as required. Taste and add honey or sugar, if using, then serve.

# mango yogurt drink
## with **fresh ginger**

Whenever I make smoothies, this recipe is always the most popular. Use very ripe fresh mangoes if available, otherwise frozen or canned mango pieces are often very good indeed. I use a variety called Alphonso, from India—regarded among aficionados as the finest mango in the world.

**1 cup mango purée, from fresh, canned, or frozen mango**
**6 ice cubes**
**1 inch fresh ginger, grated**
**1 cup low-fat yogurt**
**sparkling water, gingerale, or low-fat milk**
**sugar or honey (optional)**
**¼ cup diced fresh mango, to serve (optional)**

SERVES **4**

Put all the ingredients except the diced mango in a blender and work to a froth. Serve immediately, topped with the diced mango, if using.

# fruit ice cubes
## with **yogurt** and **honey**

Fruit juice ice cubes melt more slowly than regular ice and inject a gradual essence of fruit into other ingredients, such as yogurt, buttermilk, or even other juices. This recipe is especially delicious— yogurt with honey is one of those marriages made in heaven.

**4 cups fresh fruit juice, such as cranberry or apricot**
**sugar (optional)**
**3 cups low-fat plain yogurt**
**honey, to serve**

SERVES **4**

Make the fruit juice just a little sweeter than you like to drink it (freezing reduces sweetness), then freeze in ice cube trays.

Fill tall glasses with the fruit ice cubes and spoon in the yogurt. Drizzle honey over the top and serve.

# soy milk, nut milk, and oat milk

## breakfast smoothie
### with **banana, oat milk,** and **oat germ**

If you're not a soy milk fan, but prefer not to use dairy, try oat milk or rice milk instead: both are sold in natural food stores. Oat germ provides fiber and is also recommended if you're watching your cholesterol. A thoroughly healthy breakfast.

Put all the ingredients in a blender with 4 ice cubes. Blend until frothy.

Taste, add honey if required, then serve.

**1 large, ripe banana, chopped**
**juice of ½ lemon**
**1 tablespoon peanut butter (optional)**
**1 tablespoon oat bran or wheat germ**
**1 cup oat milk or rice milk**
**honey, to taste**

SERVES **1**

Horchata is a creamy Spanish drink made with tiger nuts. Since most of us can't easily buy tiger nuts, I have substituted cashews.

# cashew horchata

2½ cups unsalted cashews or blanched almonds
⅔ cup sugar, or to taste
4 teaspoons rose water or 1 tablespoon almond
   extract if using almonds
zest of 1 lemon, in long shreds

SERVES 4

Put the nuts in a pitcher and add 2 cups water. Cover and soak overnight in the refrigerator. Next day, put the nuts and soaking water in a blender. Add a further 2 cups water and blend until smooth. Strain through a fine sieve, pushing through as much liquid as possible. Return the nuts to the blender, add 4 cups water, blend, and strain again.

Stir the sugar and rose water or almond extract into the nut milk, then chill. Serve very cold, topped with shreds of lemon zest.

# almond flower milk

⅔ cup blanched almonds
10 ice cubes
½ cup milk
rose water or orange flower water, to taste
sugar, to taste

TO SERVE:
ice cubes
zest of ½ orange, in long shreds

SERVES 4

Put the almonds in a blender or food processor and work to a fine meal. Add the milk and 1 cup water, blend again, then strain into a pitcher. Return the almonds to the blender, add a further 1 cup water, blend again, then strain again, pushing as much liquid through the strainer as possible. Discard the nut meal (you can put through more and more water, and the milk will get thinner with each extraction). Chill. Stir in rose water or orange flower water and sweeten to taste.

To serve, put ice cubes in 4 glasses, pour in the almond milk, then serve topped with shreds of orange zest.

# coconut milk smoothie
## with **vanilla, peaches,** and **lime**

Peaches aren't tropical fruits, but they go very well with coconut milk. Other fruit such as apricots, mangoes, bananas, or papaya may be used instead.

**4 large, ripe peaches, peeled, halved, pitted, and cut into wedges**
**1 cup unsweetened coconut milk**
**a few drops of vanilla extract**
**2 tablespoons sugar, or to taste**
**6 ice cubes**
**zest of 1 lime, cut into long shreds, and freshly squeezed juice**

SERVES **2**

Put the peaches in a blender, add the coconut milk, vanilla, sugar, and ice cubes, and blend until smooth. Taste and add extra sugar if necessary.

Serve in chilled glasses, topped with a little shredded lime zest.

# mango smoothie
## with **strawberries** and **soy milk**

I love mango, but if you prefer other fruit, do use it instead. I think the strawberries are always a good idea though—their scent lifts the flavor of other fruits in a delicious fashion.

**6 ice cubes**
**2 cups fresh, canned, or frozen mango pieces**
**12 large strawberries, hulled and halved**
**freshly squeezed juice of 1 lemon**
**1 cup soy milk, or to taste**

SERVES **4**

Put the ice cubes in a blender and blend to a snow. Add the mango pieces, strawberries, and lemon juice, then pour in the soy milk with the machine running.

Add extra soy milk or water until the mixture is the thickness of light cream. Transfer to a chilled pitcher and serve in small glasses.

# raspberry smoothie
## with **soy milk**

Soy milk is a popular alternative to dairy milk. Because it has a slightly sweet taste, I find it doesn't need a sweetener—but if your sweet tooth is incurable, do add a little honey.

**2 cups raspberries**
**about 2 cups soy milk**
**12 ice cubes**
**honey, to taste**

SERVES **4**

Put the raspberries**\***, soy milk, and ice cubes in a blender and purée to a froth. Serve the honey separately so people can sweeten to taste.

**\*** If, like me, you love raspberries, reserve a few and sprinkle on top of each glass before serving.

## conversion charts

Weights and measures have been rounded up or down slightly to make measuring easier.

VOLUME EQUIVALENTS:

| American | Metric | Imperial |
|---|---|---|
| 1 teaspoon | 5 ml | |
| 1 tablespoon | 15 ml | |
| ¼ cup | 60 ml | 2 fl.oz. |
| ⅓ cup | 75 ml | 2½ fl.oz. |
| ½ cup | 125 ml | 4 fl.oz. |
| ⅔ cup | 150 ml | 5 fl.oz. (¼ pint) |
| ¾ cup | 175 ml | 6 fl.oz. |
| 1 cup | 250 ml | 8 fl.oz. |

WEIGHT EQUIVALENTS:　　MEASUREMENTS:

| Imperial | Metric | Inches | Cm |
|---|---|---|---|
| 1 oz. | 25 g | ¼ inch | 5 mm |
| 2 oz. | 50 g | ½ inch | 1 cm |
| 3 oz. | 75 g | ¾ inch | 1.5 cm |
| 4 oz. | 125 g | 1 inch | 2.5 cm |
| 5 oz. | 150 g | 2 inches | 5 cm |
| 6 oz. | 175 g | 3 inches | 7 cm |
| 7 oz. | 200 g | 4 inches | 10 cm |
| 8 oz. (½ lb.) | 250 g | 5 inches | 12 cm |
| 9 oz. | 275 g | 6 inches | 15 cm |
| 10 oz. | 300 g | 7 inches | 18 cm |
| 11 oz. | 325 g | 8 inches | 20 cm |
| 12 oz. | 375 g | 9 inches | 23 cm |
| 13 oz. | 400 g | 10 inches | 25 cm |
| 14 oz. | 425 g | 11 inches | 28 cm |
| 15 oz. | 475 g | 12 inches | 30 cm |
| 16 oz. (1 lb.) | 500 g | | |
| 2 1b. | 1 kg | | |

OVEN TEMPERATURES:

| | | |
|---|---|---|
| 110°C | (225°F) | Gas ¼ |
| 120°C | (250°F) | Gas ½ |
| 140°C | (275°F) | Gas 1 |
| 150°C | (300°F) | Gas 2 |
| 160°C | (325°F) | Gas 3 |
| 180°C | (350°F) | Gas 4 |
| 190°C | (375°F) | Gas 5 |
| 200°C | (400°F) | Gas 6 |
| 220°C | (425°F) | Gas 7 |
| 230°C | (450°F) | Gas 8 |
| 240°C | (475°F) | Gas 9 |